The World of H

The World of Hair Colour
The Art and Techniques of Modern Hair Colour

Daniel Galvin

M

Produced in association with The Hairdressing Council

First published 1977 by
THE MACMILLAN PRESS LTD
London and Basingstoke
Associated companies in Delhi Dublin
Hong Kong Johannesburg Lagos Melbourne
New York Singapore and Tokyo

Printed and bound in Great Britain by
REDWOOD BURN LIMITED
Trowbridge & Esher

British Library Cataloguing in Publication Data

Galvin, Daniel
    The world of hair colour.
    1. Hair—Dyeing and bleaching
    I. Title
    646.7′24   TT973
    ISBN 0-333-23350-6
    ISBN 0-333-23351-4 Pbk

To my wife Mavis, for all her help and patience.

Contents

Preface

It has taken me 18 years to accumulate my knowledge of hair colouring—a subject which has not previously been explored in sufficient depth—through everyday work, world-wide seminars and demonstrations and an enormous amount of research, notably in the use of vegetable colours. Through this book I want to convey to the hairdressing world in general, and particularly to the new colourists coming into the trade, the vast potential of hair colouring, so that we will all be able to provide the public with the services they deserve.

Acknowledgements

I would like to thank everyone who helped make this book possible.

My sincere gratitude goes to Vogue (U.K.), for their co-operation and kind permission for the use of photographs which have been published in their magazine.

My thanks also go to Vogue (Italy) and Vogue (U.S.A.), to Barry Lategan, David Bailey, Norman Parkinson and Clive Arrowsmith for their incredible photography.

Particular thanks to the Hairdressing Council for giving me the opportunity and encouragement for the entire concept of the book. Also to Neville Shulman, my business adviser, for his invaluable help and advice.

My sincere thanks to Wella (Great Britain) Limited, for their technical assistance and research over the years, which has helped me tremendously in the salon.

To Ray Edwards for his care and accuracy in preparing diagrams to illustrate the book.

My special thanks to Sara Thackray, editor of *Hair and Beauty,* for her unrelenting patience and dedication in helping to put my theories and ideas into words.

Lastly, but by no means least, warmest thanks to Leonard Lewis for all his faith, help and encouragement.

Introduction

IN the past, it was not necessary for most salons to have colouring specialists as this was a fairly limited field of hairdressing. But today's client is becoming increasingly colour conscious and aware of the different types and effects of colouring. Obviously, in smaller salons, there may not be enough work for a full-time colourist but there should be at least one person who specializes in colour even if they are employed in other work.

Nowadays, scope is so varied that attitudes towards hair colour have changed completely. During the 60s the majority of my work involved covering grey hair—now only 10% of my clientele have their hair coloured for this reason! Many salons are simply unaware of the potential profit from colouring.

Build on a small colouring service by starting with the ready 'grey' clientele; use permanent colours, lifting the base colour one or two shades lighter and toning the grey to create a natural effect. The next step is to introduce permanent colours to the other clients. By using a colour two or three shades lighter than their base colour you can alter the tone drastically without much of a shade change. *But,* it is important to explain the necessity of returning to the salon every month for maintenance—pointing out the cost involved!

Then promote highlighting, which is ideal for the client who wants a new look without returning to the salon every three to four weeks. Of course, there will still be some clients who remain adamant that colour will damage the hair. In these cases, I would suggest semi-permanents, colour conditioners or herbal colours (notably henna) to achieve a beautiful sheen on the hair without a noticeable colour change. This reassures clients who are either frightened of colour themselves or whose husbands, boyfriends, etc., are worried about it. Semi-permanents are also extremely successful for introducing younger clients to colour.

It is important for the colourist to have a deep understanding with the stylist—you must work *together*, respecting each other's decisions. Colour will project the line of the style so the cut must be carried out first. This may seem obvious but I know of one case where a client with long hair was first given highlights, and then had her hair cut short resulting in a polka dot effect as the hair is finer towards the ends. The colourist sells colour by working closely with the stylist—this is a key relationship in determining the success of a tinting service.

Remember that you are a professional, so have confidence in your own ability to make decisions. Psychology plays an important role in selling colour—try to understand the client's personal feelings, making quite certain that you understand each other. If the intended colour is not included on the shade chart, use colours in magazines, etc., as a guide to the tone. Listen carefully to the client's ideas—you will probably be able to build on them. Always 'play it safe'; if a client is just beginning to turn white, use a semi-permanent; if the hair is more white and she is losing her skin pigmentation, change to a permanent colour.

It was during my first worldwide demonstrations that I started to realize the huge potential of hair colouring; the problem does not lie in the products used, but in the individual knowledge of how to use them. The scope open to the hair colourist is so vast that it is impossible to learn everything—the most important thing is **always being prepared to learn!**

1. Hair Structure

THE hair is dependent, to a large extent, on genetic factors and the environmental surroundings for its structure and form. Heredity, age, physical condition and climate all contribute to colour, strength and growth of hair.

Each different hair texture determines the quality and density of colour. Example: Negroid hair is difficult to colour because of the dense natural pigmentation. So, before starting any type of hair colouring, it is essential to understand the basic structure of the hair.

Hair grows from the *follicle*—a narrow, slanting tube below the surface of the scalp. The *papilla,* a small concentration of living cells at the base of the follicle, multiply to eventually become hair. This process is known as *mitosis.* Oxygen is fed to these cells by minute blood vessels to enable the continuation of mitosis. Whilst forming and reproducing, the cells are soft but those on the outside of the group are flattened against the follicle wall.

It is these latter cells which make up the *cuticle*—hard, flattened, horny scales encircling the hair and overlapping one another. The cuticle can consist of ten strata layers depending on the texture and porosity of one single hair. The cuticle scales are bound together with a putty-like substance which produces a very strong, flexible arrangement of cells—this assists in protecting the more delicate inner layer (cortex).

The free end of the flat, overlapping scales (cuticle imbrications) points upwards in the direction of the hair growth. The protruding formation of the scales facilitates easy removal of flaking skin, dirt particles, etc. The nature of these scales allows quantities of sebum (natural oil) to become deposited as tiny reservoirs and keep a coating of sebum which is essential to keep the hair in a healthy and pliable condition.

The **cortex** (fibrous layer) is the most important layer of the hair and makes up approximately 75 to 90% of its bulk. The physical properties of the hair which depend on the cortex are:

Strength
Elasticity
Pliability
Direction of growth
Texture and quality

The cortex cells link into a continuous and elongated structure and undergo a process of *keratinization* as they are pushed up along the follicle and harden.

The central core of the hair is called the *medulla*—an irregular, honeycombed formation of soft keratin cells. Not every hair contains this, and some can have two, but this has no effect on colouring processes.

3

Hair Structure

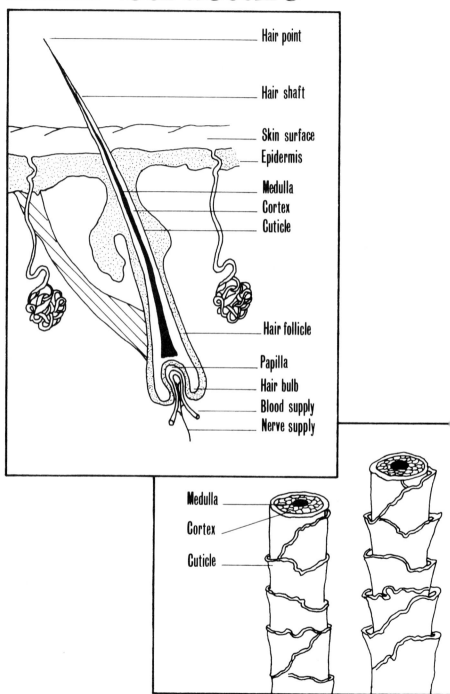

Hair point

Hair shaft

Skin surface
Epidermis

Medulla
Cortex
Cuticle

Hair follicle

Papilla
Hair bulb
Blood supply
Nerve supply

Medulla

Cortex

Cuticle

In tearing a longer section from a hair sample, as seen in this micrograph, magnified 400 times, many of the thread-like fibers within the fiber cable are removed from their original location or presumably even torn apart completely.

Hair is built up of *keratin;* protein containing sulphur, carbon, hydrogen, nitrogen and oxygen. The sulphur determines the strength of the hair because these chemical links are the most difficult to break down. Like all proteins, keratin comprises chains of amino acids (polypeptides), of which there are 22 different types.

Previously untreated hair will have these chains of polypeptides intact but if the hair has already been coloured the chains are broken. Over-processing causes the chains to break and reduce in length thereby increasing the porosity. The hair becomes extremely weak and brittle.

The Hair Cycle
Individual hairs have three stages of development (altogether taking approximately three years): anagenic, catagenic and telegenic.

1. **Anagenic** (growth) phase is the beginning of active growth and hair that is in this phase will remain on a normal head of healthy hair for 2 to 6 years. Approximately 85% of all hair on the scalp

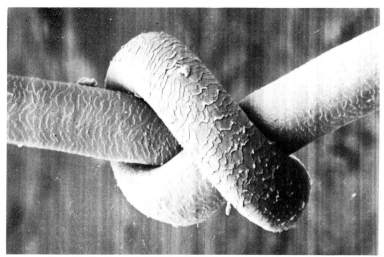

The picture above shows, magnified 400 times, a healthy, undamaged hair that has been tied into a tight knot.

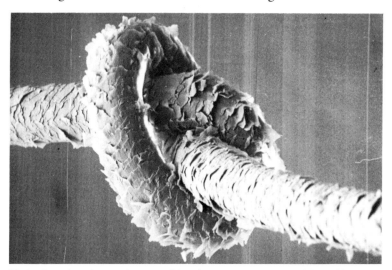

Hair that has been damaged by improper care and handling loses the binding property between the layers, as shown in the below, magnified 400 times.

is in the anagenic stage at any one time. The rate of growth and length of this period determine the maximum length of the hair. It is because of the variations in this period that some people are able to grow their hair longer than others. Contrary to popular belief, the anagenic stage is not affected by cutting, although if a client wants long hair it must be cut regularly to avoid the risk of breakage and deterioration in condition. The hair bulb is nourished by the blood circulation and provided with sensitive

The World of Hair Colour

nerve fibres so if the hair is subjected to tension during this phase a sensation of pain or discomfort is experienced.

2. **Catagenic** (transition) is the second development phase. Growth ceases in the follicle and a block of cells forms a club-like mass in the papilla. Approximately 1% of the hair only is in this transitional stage. No further growth takes place until after the final stage . . .

3. **Telegenic** (resting) phase: The follicle shrinks and the formed hair travels upwards and is held in place by the club-like mass. Approximately 14% of all hair is at any one time in the telegenic phase. After this resting period, the old hair is shed and the process repeated. The new hair either pushes up or grows past the block of cells.

Natural Pigmentation

The hair's natural colour is an inherited characteristic. The main pigment in the hair is *melanin* which is formed in the *melanocytes*. These are cells on the dermal papilla, responsible for the introduction of molecules of pigment into the cortical cells which eventually form the cortex of the hair.

Melanin starts as a colourless substance known as *tyrosine* containing small quantities of amino acids. This is acted upon by an enzyme and changes into a black pigment. The granules of pigment form in different shapes and sizes. Generally, the larger the granules the darker the hair and, conversely, the smaller the granules the lighter the hair.

Grey hair is a mixture of white (colourless) hair and the existing natural colour. This is caused by the loss of activity in the melanocytes preventing formation of melanin molecules. Greying is not necessarily due to ageing but can be attributed to serious illness, sudden shock or a lack of vitamins and mineral salts.

Infants often have beautiful blonde hair which gradually changes to a darker mousy colour when they reach puberty. This is due to the metabolic change of hormone balance.

All natural hair colour is a mixture of black, brown, red and yellow pigment.

Examples

Dark Brown hair comprises approximately the following percentages of these four colour pigments:

Black	40%
Brown	30%
Red	20%
Yellow	10%

7

Light Brown hair has less black but more yellow pigment:

Black	20%
Brown	30%
Red	20%
Yellow	30%

Natural Ash Blonde or light mousy colours are predominantly yellow:

Black	5%
Brown	5%
Red	10%
Yellow	80%

Generally, the skin is losing some of its natural pigmentation when hair starts turning white. If a client comes into the salon asking to return to her original colour it may not be advisable. Her natural colour could have suited her once but will not necessarily do so now as her complexion has probably changed.

2. Principles of Artificial Colouring

ALL artificial colours are based on one, or more, of the three primary colours: red, blue and yellow. These form the basis of the colour circle. The other colours on the circle are produced when the primary colours are mixed together. Examples: yellow+ blue = green, blue+red = purple, etc. Opposite colours on the circle neutralize each other, e.g. blue neutralizes orange and green neutralizes red.

A blue based shade should not be applied to hair with yellow tones as it could result in a greenish cast. This is because green is positioned between blue and yellow on the colour circle. The same happens if a red shade is applied to hair with yellow tones. Result? An orange cast.

The problem for the colourist is that the dye-stuffs have a varying behaviour pattern:

1. **Development Time.** Some colours develop quicker than others. The potential development rate of the colours (from the quickest) is as follows:
   Red
   Orange
   Yellow
   Purple
   Blue
   Green
   If a tint (which comprises a mixture of these colours) is under-developed there is a possibility of an irregular result. But, if the hair is given a full development time under normal conditions it will not over-develop. It is when the conditions vary, or the selection is incorrect, that the desired result will not be achieved.

2. **Tenacity** is the ability of the colours to grip and retain within the hair structure. It is interesting to note that, in order of tenacity, the colours are as follows:
   Green
   Purple
   Yellow
   Blue
   Orange
   Red
   Almost a reversal of the development rate! The texture of the hair must therefore be carefully considered before colouring. The finer

9

textures take more readily—the coarser textures resist penetration.

It is important for the student colourist to learn the manufacturers' shade charts and understand the difference between shades and tones.

Tones determine the colour of hair. A tone is a variation of a shade, e.g. Dark Blonde, Dark Ash Blonde and Dark Reddish Blonde.

Shades determine the depth of colour. The ten shades are: blue-black, black, dark brown, mid brown, light brown, dark blonde, mid blonde, light blonde, very light blonde and white.

Another point, on which I feel particularly strongly, is that you should have a basic knowledge of the chemical substances in the products being used. The professional colourist must be aware of the damaging effect they could have on the hair if used incorrectly.

pH Scale

The pH scale is a chemical gauge which determines whether a product is acid or alkaline (see diagram). pH 7 is the half-way point on the scale and is said to be neutral. From pH 6.9 down to 0.1 the scale measures acids—the lower the product reads the more acidic it is. Conversely, from pH 7.1 up to 14 the scale measures alkalis and the higher the product reads the more alkaline it is.

The pH of a product is determined by its active working substances. In refined products, a careful chemical balance is usually achieved and essential active materials are 'buffered' with other ingredients to prevent damage to the hair or skin.

The pH scale can become complex when used by chemists to measure a product—every number is a logarithmic scale of ten. This means that pH 6 is ten times more acidic than pH 7 and . . .
pH 5 is 100 times more acid than 7
pH 4 is 1,000 times more acidic than 7
pH 3 is 10,000 times more acidic than 7
pH 2 is 100,000 times more acidic than 7
pH 1 is 1,000,000 times more acidic than 7
It may sound frightening when I say pH 1 is one million times more acidic than pH 7 but everyday foods, for instance, often have a very low pH. Example: Orange juice has a pH of 2. The contents of the stomach, which contain hydrochloric acid, can measure as low as pH 1!

On the alkaline side of the scale . . .
pH 8 is 10 times more alkaline than 7
pH 9 is 100 times more alkaline than 7
pH 10 is 1,000 times more alkaline than 7
pH 11 is 10,000 times more alkaline than 7
pH 12 is 100,000 times more alkaline than 7
pH 13 is 1,000,000 times more alkaline than 7
pH 14 is 10,000,000 times more alkaline than 7
If you compare pH 1 to pH 13 you will find that it is ten billion times more acid. Conversely, pH 13 is ten billion times more alkaline than pH 1!

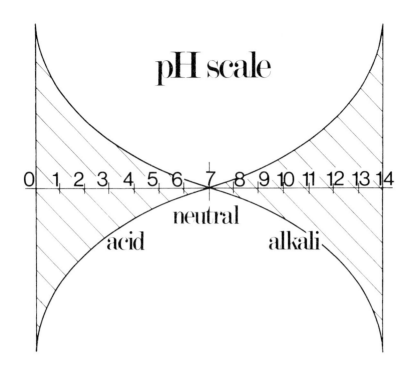

pH scale

0 1 2 3 4 5 6 7 8 9 10 11 12 13 14

neutral

acid   alkali

The most accurate way of reading pH is with a pH meter. This comprises electrodes which measure the concentration of hydrogen ions on the alkaline side. An ion is an electrically charged atom—ions are attracted to the two types of electrode on a pH meter: cathode and anode. The balance of readings from these two electrodes gives the pH reading.

The pH of hair and skin is determined by the sebum and sweat which make up the acid mantle. The actual pH of hair and skin varies from one person to another but will generally be acid at a pH of 4.5 to 5.5.

Tints and bleaches are always alkaline and cannot work on the outer part of the hair structure—they have to penetrate the hair shaft. How? These products have to open the cuticle of the hair shaft to enable active materials to penetrate to the inner part of the hair. This is only possible if the products are alkaline. The *concentration* of alkaline materials and other 'buffer' ingredients determines how long the penetration and opening of the hair will take. If this process is carried out too quickly, hair damage will occur.

11

3. Choosing a Colour

THE purpose of hair is to protect the scalp; it is not necessarily a beauty asset and can therefore be tremendously enhanced by the perceptive and imaginative use of colourants. I am not suggesting that people should change their hair colour completely. On the contrary, by only slightly changing the colour to accentuate the natural pigment, the hair colour will, in turn, promote the size and colour of the eyes and the colour of the complexion. The art of hair colouring is knowing which colour to use and whether or not it will *suit* the client.

When choosing a colour, it is important to consider the depth of pigmentation in the base colour. Example: Apply a light ash blonde to dark brown and the result will be a bright chestnut brown. This is caused by the peroxide in the tint reducing the black/brown natural pigments, thus projecting the natural red/yellow pigments. Incidentally, this is the hardest of all colours to remove whether painting a wall, dyeing a dress or colouring hair.

Personally, I feel that if the colour is going to be that difficult to achieve, it is not likely to suit the client and therefore should not have been chosen. I particularly recommend a colour which is two or three shades lighter than the natural shade to emphasize the natural pigment.

Skin Test

With the exception of vegetable products such a henna, all permanent dyes have a toxic base (mainly para-phenylene diamines, diamino benzenes and toluene diamines). It is therefore essential to give every client a skin test 48 hours before each colour application—to ensure she is not allergic to these particular chemicals. Although a client may not develop an allergy the first time, there is a possibility that she could be allergic on a subsequent occasion (just as people can suddenly develop an allergy to a perfume which they have been using happily for the last 20 years). Remember: Colourists need only ONE client who is not given a skin test prior to permanent colouring to put them out of business!

Method

Using the skin just behind the ear, apply the tint to an area the size of a 5p piece. Go ahead with colouring if no swelling or irritation occurs within 48 hours. Do not colour if the client shows an allergy (no harm will have been done by the skin test).

Effects of a para colour application to a client with an allergy are horrific. Initial symptoms are irritation of the head and then the face which subsequently swells up to twice its normal size—or even three times the size in extreme cases. The swelling spreads to the rest of the body resulting in severe blistering and weeping; the client will also suffer bad headaches, a dryness in the mouth and hot and cold shivers as with influenza.

Before making the final decision on which shade to choose, talk to the client about her own views on colour. If you disagree, tactfully explain *why*, pointing out the colour of her eyes, her complexion and, without going to extremes, her life-style.

It is important to have confidence in your decision as this will instil confidence in the client. If you are changing the colour fairly drastically, it is advisable to warn the client beforehand that it will take her a while to become accustomed to her new image. If a client insists on a colour against your will, ask her to sign a statement recording your recommendations in writing to safeguard yourself. As a professional, rely on your own judgement and try not to be motivated by the salon till—after all, what you lose on the swings today you will gain on the roundabouts tomorrow through recommendations.

Note: Always ensure the client has enough time to have her hair coloured. There is no short cut to hair colouring—it is not simply a matter of 'sloshing' it on and washing it off. In order to achieve the best results, an enormous amount of care must be taken in application, development time and conditioning. Obviously, clients are impatient whilst waiting for the colour to develop so make sure they have sufficient magazines, tea, coffee and sandwiches, etc. In other words, MAKE A FUSS OF THEM!

When not to use Permanent Colour

Never use a permanent colour if any of the following are apparent:
1. Abrasions or skin diseases.
2. Metallic substances have previously been used on the hair (e.g. compound henna which leaves a dull, metallic hue).
3. Over-processing due to straightening, perming or bleaching.
4. Hair has just been permed—always allow a period of seven days between perming and tinting or the perm will be slackened and the hair damaged.
5. Hair has recently been highlighted.
6. It will not suit the client's complexion, eyes or life-style.

Always use your professional opinion to judge what has previously been used on the hair. Never take the client's word for it! *If in any doubt at all—do not colour.*

Client Record Card

name   --

address --

-- tel. ----------------------

natural colour   --

date of pre-test --

DATE	SHADE Nos.	PEROXIDE VOL.	DEVELOPMENT PERIOD	REMARKS		COLOURIST	STYLIST

Preparing the Client for Colour

Hair colouring is a messy business so make sure the client's clothing is well protected with a gown, cape and towel around her neck and shoulders before starting work. It is also extremely important to protect your hands so *always* wear gloves, well-sprinkled inside with talcum powder, to avoid the risk of skin irritation. Remember: Your hands are the tools of your trade—without them you have no trade—so it is worth looking after them!

Salon Lighting

It is essential to work where you can *see*, whether in good artificial light or natural light. It is only possible to register the true tone of colour in natural light. Some salon lights throw red or orange glows on freshly tinted hair and this can alarm the client, especially if an ash shade has been chosen. Under these circumstances, hold a magazine, or anything with a flat surface, 20 inches above the client's head and this will 'kill' all the red light on the hair. Always warn the client beforehand if the salon lighting will distort the results. For specialist guidance on the best artificial lighting consult the leading lighting manufacturers.

Record Card System

One of the most successful ways of organizing a hair colouration department is to keep a record card on every client (see p. 00). Each time a client visits the salon her personal file can be checked and a new entry inserted. The cards, which are filed in alphabetical order, should include the names of the client, stylist and colourist, what, where and when colour was applied and details of aftercare. The cards must be kept up to date every time the client comes into the salon for any colour application. In the event of a client wanting a colour that she had, say, two years ago, the colourist immediately knows the exact range and shade by referring to the relevant record card.

4. Different Types of Colouring

HAIR colouring products fall into three main categories:

1. **Temporary.** Artificial colour is applied to the hair and forms a loose connection with the outside layer, thereby producing a tone. This is easily washed off.

2. **Semi-permanent.** A greater resistance to water is achieved by using a fluid which suspends minute molecules of colour, resulting in deeper penetration of the cuticle layers. Thus semi-permanent colours have greater durability than temporary colours.

3. **Permanent.** The artificial pigment penetrates right through the cuticle into the cortex where it becomes oxidised and integrates into the hair structure so that it is virtually permanent.

Temporary Colour

Temporary water rinses are the mildest form of hair colouring and should wash out with the first shampoo. These rinses adhere to the surface of the hair shaft. The colour granules are too large to penetrate the hair so it is really like coating the hair with colour.

This type of colourant is particulary useful for the client with an abundance of white hair which is either slightly discoloured or has yellowish tinges—caused by the atmosphere or smoking. They will enhance the natural hair colour without actually changing the basic colour.

Temporary colours will also add depth to tinted hair that has faded in the sun between root retouching. It is important not to over-apply these colourants as they coat the hair and can have a dulling effect.

Application

There are two types of temporary rinse:

1. *Traditional Method.* Add coloured drops, according to depth required, to extremely hot water. Using an application brush, apply to hair which has previously been shampooed and towel-dried. Take fine sections from the nape of the neck upwards to the front hairline, pounding the colour on to the roots as this is the most resistant part of the hair.

2. *Modern Pre-mixed Rinses.* No mixing is necessary. Simply apply liberally over the entire head, simultaneously combing through the hair to ensure an even result. Pre-mixed rinses can also contain conditioning agents, or setting lotions, or both.

Semi-permanent Colour

Keypoint: Semi-permanent rinses can only *add* colour to the hair. Is impossible to use these colourants to lighten the hair because they are not mixed with hydrogen peroxide. The semi-permanent granules penetrate the inner cuticle of the hair, not altering the natural pigments in the cortex but achieving a richer base colour. Semi-permanent colours last from four to six shampoos, gradually fading away before they completely wash out.

This type of rinse is invaluable as a colour refreshener. It is ideal for the client who does not want to actually change her hair colour but simply brighten it. It is also extremely effective when colouring dry, porous hair, creating a beautiful sheen in addition to enhancing the colour.

Semi-permanent rinses often provide the answer for disguising white hair, particularly if the client has not previously had a colour treatment. However, it is important to remember that these rinses do not cover the hair completely—usually there is only up to 50% coverage. Example: If a dark brown semi-permanent rinse is applied to dark brown greying hair, the result will be light brown lights on a dark brown base.

Equipment

Semi-permanent Colour
Bowl
Sponge

Application

Shampoo hair as normal and towel dry to remove any excess water.

Permanent Colour

Permanent hair colours are known as *oxidation* dyes because hydrogen peroxide is added in order to activate the colour. These dyes are made up of small molecules of colour which penetrate the hair cuticle and then react with the hydrogen peroxide causing the molecules to expand within the cortex, becoming too large for removal.

Hydrogen Peroxide

The amount of peroxide to be used is decided by the colour manufacturers and *must* be firmly adhered to. The base colour of

18

1. Apply colour at the backwash, using a sponge to ensure even distribution over the head.

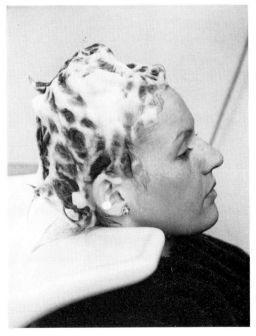

2. Massage into a foamy lather and leave to develop for 15 to 20 minutes. Rinse thoroughly.

the hair determines the strength of the peroxide: 10 volume (3%) and 20 volume (6%) are toning peroxides, 30 volume (9%) and 40 volume (12%) are lifting peroxides and 60 volume (18%) is maximum lifting peroxide. In other words, the lighter the colour required, the stronger the peroxide and the darker the colour, the weaker the peroxide.

Warning: Never use a higher volume of peroxide than necessary as this will damage the hair and create the wrong colour. If you happen to run out of one particular volume, either dilute a higher volume to the desired strength with distilled water or accurately mix a higher and lower peroxide together, e.g. 1 oz. 20 vol. (6%) + 1 oz. 40 vol. (12%) = 2 oz. 30 vol. (9%).

Permanent colours are extremely versatile as they can achieve a lighter or darker colour but, in my opinion, hair should not be tinted darker than the natural colour as this kills the natural highlights and results in a flat, dull finish.

When using a permanent colour, I always mix two or three tints together with peroxide; one to lift, one to colour and one to give depth or, in the case of white hair, to cover. *But* this has come with years of practice and I would not advise an inexperienced colourist to attempt it.

Equipment

Permanent Colour
Hydrogen peroxide
Measure
Bowl
Tinting brush
Comb
Strips of cotton wool
Barrier cream
Timer
Gloves

Application

Mix tint, using a measure to ensure the accurate amount of hydrogen peroxide is added to the colour. In the case of a first-time whole head tint, begin by applying the colour to the middle lengths and ends. Apply colour to the roots after the middle lengths and ends have been left for the manufacturers' recommended development time. Always take care not to create a build up of colour on the hairline as this is the weakest part of the hair and may 'grab' colour, producing a heavy effect.

1. Start applying the tint at the nape, brushing it on to the hair within 1 inch of the roots.

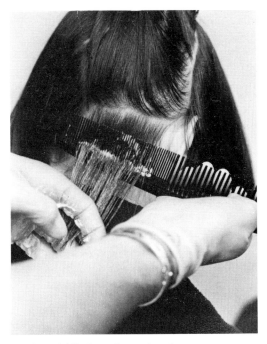

2. Comb the tint through the middle lengths and ends.

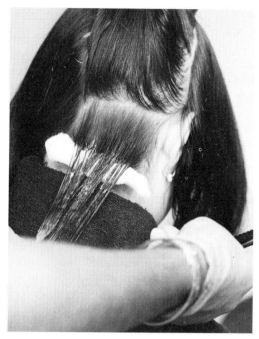

3. Place strips of cotton wool underneath each section to prevent the colour reaching the roots too quickly . . .

4. . . . covering the entire head as shown. Leave for the manufacturers' recommended development time before . . .

5. . . . applying tint to the roots (using the regrowth method on page
   25) and comb through without pressing the hair against the
   head so the colour has an opportunity to develop evenly. Leave for
   the manufacturers' recommended development time.

Rinse off with lukewarm water (it can be harmful if the water is
too hot) and shampoo if directed by the manufacturers' instructions.
A timer should be used to ensure the recommended development
time is carefully followed. The experienced colourist will find an
accelerator a great asset to speed up the development time in every
form of colouring, but it is not advisable for the beginner.

The experienced colourist may also choose to tint in three stages
instead of two. Example: Apply colour to the middle lengths and
ends 2 inches away from the roots, then apply within 1 inch of the
roots, before applying to the roots for the remainder of the
development period. (See figure 4.1.)

Total Development Time

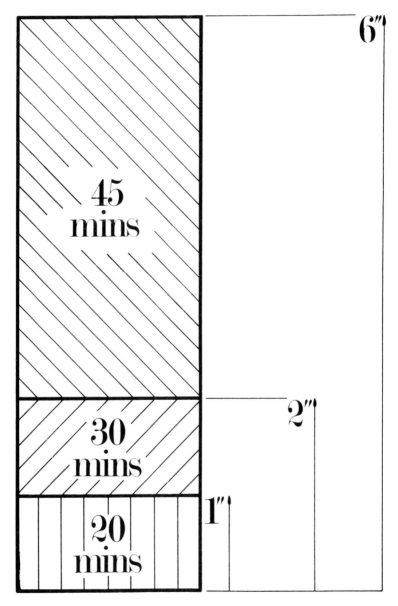

Figure 4.1

Regrowth Tinting

Once a client has a permanent colour she will require a regrowth tint approximately every four weeks.

Equipment

Permanent Colour
Hydrogen peroxide
Measure
Bowl
Tinting brush
Barrier cream
Timer
Gloves

Application

Mix tint as with whole head permanent colour. If the tint is fairly dark, use a barrier cream on the skin around the edge of the hairline at the front. (This is not necessary with a blonde tint.)

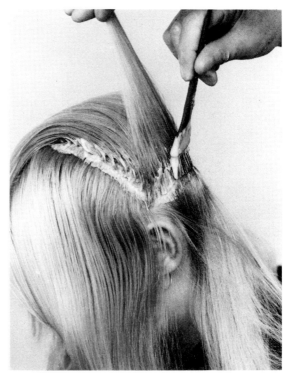

1. Taking ¼ inch sections, carefully apply the tint to the roots with a tinting brush, starting at the crown and working downwards to the nape.

2. Repeat on the front sections, working downwards from the top of the head. The lengths are held out at 90 degrees to the head and the tint is applied to the roots on either side of the sections. Take care not to overlap the existing tinted hair.

3. When colour has been applied, section the hair in the opposite direction to check even distribution of colour. Comb hair back off the face and leave for the manufacturers' recommended development time. Rinse off with lukewarm water and shampoo if recommended.

Tinting Long Hair

When a client has long hair, I generally prefer to *massage* colour through the lengths rather than combing as this avoids any stretching or breakage. It is also a more effective method of manoeuvring colour through the hair to create an even overall tone.

I always try to keep movement in the colour by graduating to a slightly lighter colour at the ends. After all, the professional colourist receives most praise when other people do not realize the client's hair has even been coloured!

The following table summarizes the principles, requirements, permanence, advantages and disadvantages of the three main types of hair colourant.

Type of Colour	Principle	Requirement	Permanence	Advantages	Disadvantages
Temporary	Adheres to surface of hair shaft.	Instant change but instant removal.	One shampoo.	Easy to use. Easily removed if client not satisfied.	Washes off. Dulling effect if over-applied.
Semi-permanent	Diffusion of small molecules in cuticle.	Colour refreshener. Disguises grey hair. Slight shade change.	4 to 6 shampoos.	Easy to use.	Can only add colour. Fades. Only 50% coverage.
Permanent	Diffusion of small molecules in cortex where they become oxidized.	Permanent colour change. Hair can be lightened. Covers grey hair.	Does not wash out.	Complete cover. Range of colour.	Time-consuming to apply. Skin test. Regrowth.

Other Colouring Techniques

Brightening Shampoo

A brightening shampoo will bring out the natural highlights in the hair—ideal for the client who wants to keep the 'sun' look all the year round. It is only advisable, however, once every three months otherwise a more drastic colour change will take place. Mix two parts of 20 vol. (6%) peroxide to one part shampoo and add two drops of .880 ammonia. Apply as a first shampoo at the backwash,

27

leaving on the middle lengths and ends for five minutes and then massage over the entire head for two minutes. Rinse and shampoo again.

Colour Bath

During the period between colouring applications, where loss of pigmentation has occurred, I often apply a colour bath which is formulated from equal parts of hair colour, 20 vol. (6%) peroxide and shampoo. This method is far kinder to the hair than re-tinting to add colour between treatments and it is of paramount importance to keep the hair in good condition.

Successful results can also be achieved on previously untreated hair within one or two shades either side of the natural colour by using this method. A colour bath will last for up to six weeks before re-application.

Pre-pigmentation

I devised the pre-pigmentation method for toning hair back down to its natural colour without first 'filling' with red pigment. Pre-pigmentation is effective when a client's hair colour has faded, is sun-bleached or if she merely wishes to return to her natural colour.

How does it work? Say, for example, the client's hair is pale yellow and her natural colour is light brown. Pick out the natural shade by checking the regrowth and then mix a colour two shades darker, which, in this case, would be dark brown. Mix one part tint to three parts water, apply to the hair and leave for ten minutes. The hair is then 'shock neutralised' (post-oxidized) by adding 6 vol. (1.8%) peroxide—using an equal quantity to the amount of water previously mixed to the colour. By neutralising in this way, the colourist achieves a longer-lasting result and avoids any trace of khaki tones in the hair. This method can also be used on any hair colour up to the shade of yellow.

I have already explained how the permanent colour pigments enter the hair shafts and expand individually as they develop their colour. But, if the hair is in a highly porous condition, the colour can completely wash out as the cuticle will not hold it. Pre-pigmentation is highly successful in retarding this colour loss from porous hair because the pigment molecules fuse together in the cortex. (Figure 4.2.)

Porosity

Reasons for porosity:
1. Excess of sun combined with chlorinated or salt water during swimming.
2. Over-processing from straightening, perming, tinting or bleaching.
3. Scorching by hair dryer.

Pre-pigmentation

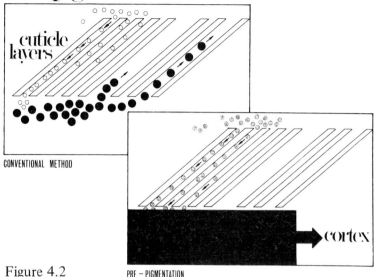

cuticle
layers

CONVENTIONAL METHOD

cortex

Figure 4.2   PRE – PIGMENTATION

Test for Porosity

Take a few strands of the client's hair and slide your thumb up the hair shaft towards the root. If the hair feels rough and resists this action it is probably porous. Also feel the hair when it is wet; porous hair will be extremely soft with a similar texture to cotton wool and will stretch unnaturally.

It is impossible to achieve an even colour on porous hair by using a single colour. Two processes must be employed; one colour should be used on the roots where the hair is stronger, and for the middle lengths and ends use a colour bath, semi-permanent rinse or pre-pigmentation. Example: A client has slightly greying, mid-brown porous hair. Choose a dark ash blonde shade for the roots, then use the pre-pigmentation method, with a dark warm blonde and light brown shade, for the lengths and ends. This will create an even colour.

Burn-out

If a permanent colour is left on the hair for longer than the manufacturers' recommended development time, the peroxide will have a slight bleaching effect and reduce the artificial colour agent, producing a slightly lighter result at the roots than intended. This is known as burn-out. It will also adversely effect the hair's condition—so never allow it to happen!

5. Colour Correction

OCCASIONALLY, a client comes into the salon with a heavy deposit of artificial pigmentation in her hair. In these cases, I prefer to use a highlifting, colourless tint rather than strip the colour out with bleach to make it one or two shades lighter. The result is a softer colour effect and it is kinder to the hair. This method is also useful when treating hairlines that 'grab' colour.

The best method of restoring colour to hair that has been reddened by the sun is to apply a solution of concentrated ash-mixed tones, mixed with the normal amount of peroxide and an equal quantity of water. This should be applied with a brush, as a rinse, and left for a maximum of 20 minutes. (The length of time is determined by the depth of the desired colour.)

The same method can be employed when hair is too ash, which often occurs when the incorrect colour has previously been applied. A concentrated red tone should then be used. This treatment lasts for up to six weeks before re-application is necessary.

Examples of Colour Failures

1. Colour is too heavy on the ends of the hair.

   Reason: Hair is over-porous, possibly due to straightening, or excessive perming or tinting. The tint may have been combed through the hair too quickly which results in a colour build up.

   Correction: The ends can be lifted by a mild mixture of powder bleach, peroxide and shampoo. Avoid creating reddish tones in ash shades. Alternatively, a highlifting tint can be used on dry hair.

2. Colour is too dark and heavy at the hairline in brown shades or too ash in blonde shades.

   Reason: Hair is finer around the face (and lighter if it is a blonde shade) so it will accept colours and ash tones more readily.

   Correction: Use a lighter shade of tint around the face (a lesser ash shade in blonde tones), or apply a highlifting tint around the face on top of the original application, or brush a mild powder bleach around the hairline after the tint has been rinsed off the hair. Again, beware of causing reddish tones.

3. Insufficient coverage of white hair.

   Reason: The tint chosen was either too ash or had not been given enough time to develop. The hair may be extremely resistant to colour.

   Correction: Choose a warmer shade of tint or, if the tone seems correct, try a stronger volume of peroxide to break the hair down and pick a slightly deeper shade of tint.

4. Dark spots appear in blonde shades.

Reason: This occurs if the tint is badly mixed when ash concentrate is used with a base shade.

Correction: The spots will gradually fade with shampooing. They can be lifted slightly with very careful application of powder bleach mixture.

5. Colour is faded on the ends of the hair immediately after tinting.

Reason: Either the tint was not combed through quickly enough or the hair is porous and rejects the tint.

Correction: If the hair is in good condition, comb the tint through sooner. But if the hair is porous from perming or sun-bleaching, the colour can usually be revived by the use of pre-pigmentation, colour baths or a semi-permanent rinse. These can also be successfully used to revive colour between tint applications.

6. Overall colour is too light or dark.

Reason: An incorrect formula has been chosen, or the wrong record card has been identified for the client, or the tint has been over- or under-processed.

Correction: a. Too dark; a slight lift in tone may be achieved by a shampoo plus a small quantity of powder bleach with peroxide but it is better to allow the colour to fade naturally. b. Too light; either re-tint hair, if scalp is not over-sensitive, or tone down by pre-pigmentation or a colour bath.

7. Colour does not appear to be developing.

Reason: It is possible that the peroxide has weakened in strength or the incorrect proportions of tint and peroxide have been used.

Correction: Re-tint as soon as the scalp is in an acceptable condition. If in doubt, test peroxide strength. Always *concentrate* whilst mixing in order to achieve the right consistency.

8. Colour is successful after application but changes during the following week.

Reason: Hair is probably over-porous and, although shampooed thoroughly, colour particles still deposited in the hair shaft carry on working.

Correction: Use a pH balancer or anti-oxidant cream after shampooing.

9. Hair that was originally highlighted successfully becomes too blonde and the condition deteriorates.

Reason: The hair has been repeatedly over-highlighted. The bleach may have been taken through the complete lengths of the hair at each application.

Correction: The highlights must not be repeated so frequently. There should be *at least* three months between each application and then only the regrowth must be treated.

10. Natural hair between highlights has an orange/red cast and the regrowth is extremely obvious.

Reason: An oxidation toner has been used on highlights.

Correction: Where a toner is necessary avoid oxidation colours. A water rinse will cut down the red tones.

11. Colour has too many orange or red tones.

Reason: Either an insufficient amount of ash concentrate has been used or the incorrect basic formula was chosen.

Correction: a. Darker shades; use a rinse of ash concentrate and low volume of peroxide but watch carefully to ensure that hair does not turn too dark. b. Blonde shades; a water rinse should be used.

12. The hair has a green cast.

Reason: This usually occurs when toning bleached hair to a deeper shade.

Correction: Counteract by toning down with pre-pigmentation to avoid khaki tones. Semi-permanent rinses, in warm shades, are usually successful if carefully applied.

13. Half way through the development period, the hair is already turning too dark.

Reason: Incorrect colour choice or the peroxide is too weak.

Correction: Choose a colour which is four shades lighter than the one used. Mix as normal and apply over the top of the previous colour to prevent the density of the initial pigmentation developing fully.

Obviously, prevention is better than cure! But, nobody is perfect and it is therefore essential to be prepared to correct mistakes without the client ever having been aware of them.

For example, on one occasion when I first started colouring, I was working on two clients simultaneously; one had just been bleached and was waiting for the toner application and the other had brown hair and was waiting for the tint to be applied to her roots. I mixed the two colours—light ash blonde and light ash brown which had a blue ash base. As I was particularly busy, I asked an assistant to apply the light ash brown tint. In error, she applied it to the client with a highly bleached base and the result was a rapid development of a navy blue tone! I immediately told her to rinse the colour off and then re-applied the bleach, which was still mixed in a bowl, and within seconds the colour was lifted out. I then applied the correct toner and achieved the desired result. The client was totally unaware that anything had occurred and not only left the salon happily satisfied, but is still a regular client of mine today!

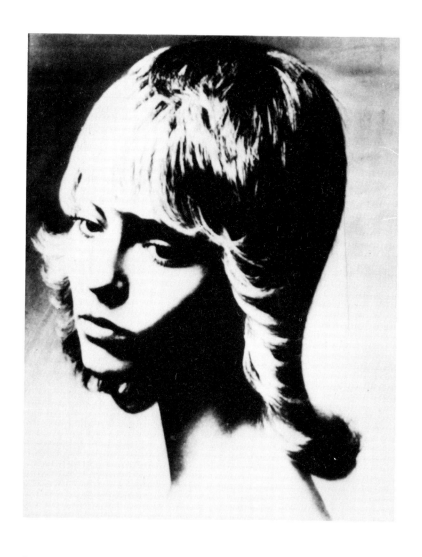

By permission of VOGUE, copyright © Conde Nast Publications Limited.
Photograph by Clive Arrowsmith. Hair by Leonard, colour by Daniel.

6. Bleaching

PERSONALLY, I never bleach the entire head because, as I have already mentioned, only the colours which are two or three shades lighter than the client's natural pigmentation will suit her complexion and this can be achieved without the use of bleach. Even if her hair is only bleached two or three shades lighter, the result will be an overall 'flat' colour from roots to ends. The hair will *look* dyed and lose all its natural movement (everybody has between two and six shades and tones of natural highlights in their hair).

If the client wants a more drastic colour change to a lighter colour, her natural shade should not be darker than a mousy base for the colour to suit her. If a client with a dark blonde to light ash brown base particularly wants to change to blonde, I would use a strong lightening tint and lift the hair up to six shades lighter—still keeping the natural movement.

However, this said, it is important for the colourist to be competent in every type of hair colouring process and, once experienced, you will be able to make your own decisions about the methods you use.

Pre-bleaching is the removal of pigmentation by an oxidation process; bleach is based on ammonia releasing agents and is mixed with hydrogen peroxide. As there is no colour pigment in bleach, the action is purely ammonia+peroxide. Together they bleach out the natural pigment in the hair. How much bleaching takes place depends on the following:

1. Even distribution of bleach applied to the hair.
2. Length of time the bleach is left on the hair (the longer, the better the lift).
3. Strength of peroxide used but remember that the higher the strength, the greater the potential damage.
4. Natural hair colour; the darker the hair, the less likely it is that the colourist will achieve a very 'white' result.
5. Strength of the hair structure.

Hydrogen Peroxide

The chemical formula for hydrogen peroxide is H_2O_2; 2 atoms of hydrogen+2 atoms of oxygen = an unstable compound. Because of the oxygen molecules, there is a high oxygen activity so when peroxide is used in bleaching it is important to make sure the peroxide has been correctly stabilized.

It is a good idea for every salon to invest in a hydrometer (an instrument for measuring the specific gravity of liquid); the strength of the peroxide can then be continually checked. Always check new containers of peroxide in case they have been marked with the incorrect volume or have been standing for a long time at the suppliers. *Never leave the top off a peroxide container for any length of time.*

Bleaching is used to achieve the correct base shade in preparation for toning. Example: A client with light brown hair wants an ash blonde shade. Bleach the hair to remove all the natural pigmentation until it is a pale lemon. It is then a suitable base for an ash blonde toner.

Compatibility Test

Take a cutting of the client's hair and drop it into a solution of peroxide and ammonia: 2 ozs. of 20 vol. (6%) peroxide + 2 drops of ammonia. If the hair chemically reacts the solution will heat up and effervesce; the hair will probably turn yellow within minutes. If this occurs it is an indication that the hair is contaminated with metal. In these cases do not bleach or use any permanent colour on the hair. If you are still in any doubt, take another cutting and apply the complete bleaching and toning process to it. Obviously this will be time-consuming so ask the client to return to the salon the following day or week.

Equipment
Oil bleach
Hydrogen peroxide
Measure
Bowl
Tinting brush
Strips of cotton wool
Timer

Application
Mix the bleach and peroxide carefully. For a first time entire head application, take ½ inch sections and apply the bleach to the middle lengths and ends. Place strips of cotton wool in between the sections to avoid inadvertently getting the bleach onto the roots of the hair. Heat from the scalp causes the roots to develop quicker so if the bleach is applied to the entire head initially, the roots would be lighter than the rest of the hair.

After the middle lengths and ends have developed for the manufacturers' recommended time for a first time head, remove the strips of cotton wool and apply the bleach to the roots. Leave for the recommended development period.

Although it is possible to use an accelerator to speed up bleaching, it is not advisable because the heat expansion of the bleaching material could easily cause breakage.

Rinse the hair thoroughly in lukewarm water and shampoo well because any deposit left in the hair will prevent the toner from developing. Ensure all bleach is removed from the hairline. Conditioning is important at this stage—it will make the hair more manoeuvrable and it should make it easier to apply the toner.

Towel-blot the hair to take out excess water. In order to avoid the overall 'flat' colour which often results, I suggest picking out a few strands of hair at random and wrapping them in aluminium foil. Then apply the toner to the middle lengths and ends for approximately ten minutes before applying to the roots for a further fifteen minutes, depending on the porosity of the hair. Unwrap the foil and apply the toner to the strands to achieve colour variation. Leave for approximately another five minutes. Rinse thoroughly and shampoo in the normal way.

Note: Bleaching can be damaging to the hair so subsequent restructural treatments are extremely important.

Regrowth Bleaching

It is essential to be very precise when applying a regrowth bleach, taking care not to overlap sections which have previously been bleached. Twice the number of sections should be taken for bleaching than for a permanent tint, otherwise breakage and uneven colour may result.

Start taking very fine horizontal sections from the crown downwards. Hold the sections out at 45 degrees to the head to ensure the lengths and ends are not pressed into the bleach. Leave on the hair for the recommended time, checking periodically, and then rinse and shampoo in the normal way before applying the toner. Towel blot the hair and apply the toner to the roots of the hair only for ten to fifteen minutes because this hair is more resistant as it is freshly bleached hair. Then apply the toner to the middle lengths and ends of the hair and leave for a further ten to fifteen minutes, according to the manufacturers' recommended development time, to achieve an even result.

It is not advisable to perm over-bleached hair as this will cause a breakdown in the hair structure and the hair will not readily accept colour as the outer cuticle would be almost non-existent! It is safer to apply perms to tinted hair in good condition.

Bleaching Highlights

Although I am opposed to bleaching an entire head, I am in favour of bleached highlights. What is the difference? If a client has whole head bleach, a 20 volume peroxide has been mixed with the bleach before application. An oxidation toner is then also applied— together making a total of 40 volume peroxide mixed with products used on the hair. This figure escalates every month as the client returns for retouching until, after a period of a year, it reaches the following: 40 volume peroxide mixed with the products applied to the roots, and 260 volume peroxide used to achieve the effect on the end of the hair!

But, in the case of bleached highlights, a 20 volume peroxide solution is used for the highlights and, after a year, the client has still only had 20 volume peroxide used to achieve the highlights in her hair.

By permission of Innoxa (England) Limited.
Hair by Leonard.
Colour by Daniel.

Photograph of Barbara Bach by Clive Arrowsmith.
Dress by Zandra Rhodes.
Hair by Leonard.
Colour by Daniel.

By permission of Revlon.
Hair by Leonard.
Colour by Daniel

By permission of VOGUE, copyright © Condé Nast Publications Limited.
Photograph by Clive Arrowsmith.
Hair by Leonard.
Colour by Daniel.

Photograph by Barry Lategan.
Hair by Leonard.
Colour by Daniel.

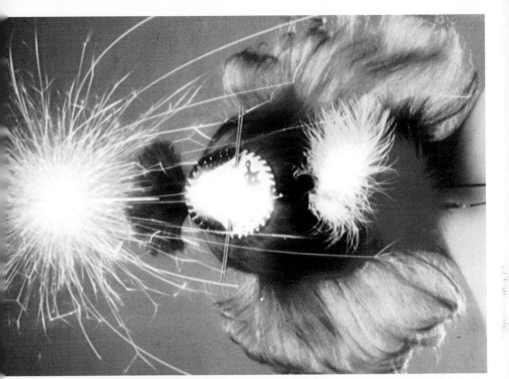

By permission of VOGUE, copyright ©Condé Nast Publications Limited.
Photographs by Barry Lategan.
Hair by Leonard.
Colour by Daniel.

By permission of VOGUE Italia.
Photograph by Barry Lategan.
Hair by Leonard.
Colour by Daniel.

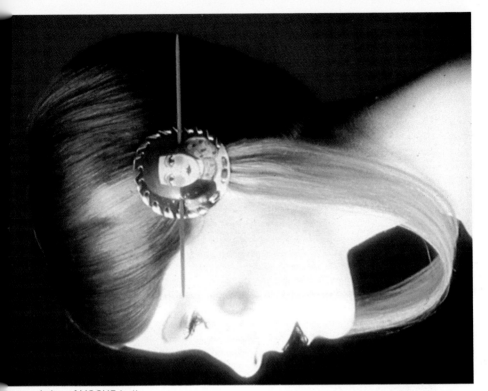

By permission of VOGUE, copyright © Condé Nast Publications Limited.
Photograph by Barry Lategan.
Hair by Leonard.
Colour by Daniel.

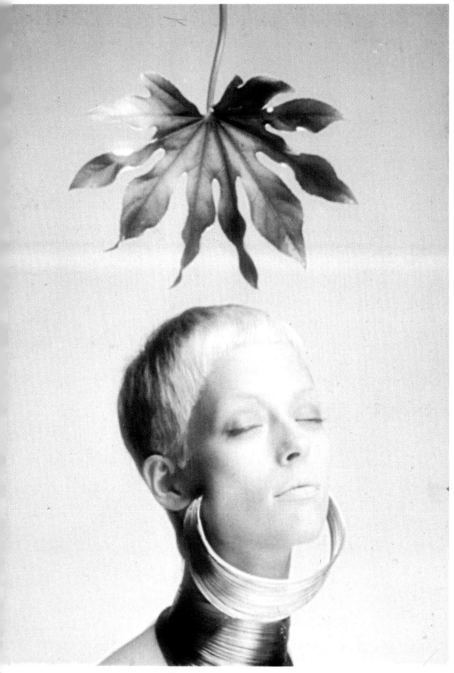

By permission of VOGUE Beauty Book, copyright © Condé Nast Publications Limited.
Photograph by Barry Lategan.
Hair by Leonard.
Colour by Daniel.

7. Highlighting

HIGHLIGHTING is probably the most natural-looking effect that can be achieved with hair colour. Ironically, it is also one of the oldest methods of colouring. Early records show that it was used by Venetian women working in the fields; they pulled strands of hair through small holes in their straw hats, applied lemon juice or chamomile, and bleached them in the sun!

But it was only comparatively recently that highlighting became fashionable. At the end of the Second World War, the Parisiennes started having highlights in their hair using the silver foil method. In the early 60s the Americans introduced a time-saving method of highlighting with a plastic cap which is still commonly used today.

Traditional Cap Method

Equipment

Bleach
Hydrogen peroxide
Measure
Polythene highlighting cap
Crochet hook
Tinting brush
Bowl

Application

Comb hair into the position it is normally worn. Fix the polythene cap securely over the head and use a crochet hook to pick out strands of hair through the holes in the cap. (If caps are soiled or the holes enlarged, discard them immediately. Never use polythene bags without manufactured holes because they may tear—causing blobs on the roots of the hair.)

Starting at the front hairline, take even sections, making sure no strand overlaps another to avoid a striped finish. Mix bleach and hydrogen peroxide into a thick paste to stop penetration through the holes. Apply to the hair generously, but be careful not to press the bleach on to the cap.

Leave for 20 to 30 minutes, depending on the base colour, until the desired colour is obtained. Rinse thoroughly and, if using an oxidizing toner for highlights, give the hair one light shampoo and apply desired toner *before* removing the cap. If the toner is allowed to touch the natural colour it will spoil the finished effect. Finally, rinse off the toner, remove the cap and shampoo normally. If, however, a semi-permanent toner is used, remove the cap before application.

Disadvantages

In my opinion, far too much guesswork is involved in the cap method. The highlights are difficult to achieve close to the parting. There is no guarantee of the strand thickness—which creates an uneven balance of highlights.

As with most things worth achieving in life, highlights can only be professionally perfected by devoting extra time and effort to them. This is why I have devised my own method of weaving the hair for highlighting. Admittedly, it is time-consuming so your charges should be altered accordingly.

Weaving Method

Equipment

Bleach
Hydrogen peroxide
Measure
Bowl
Strips of aluminium foil
Tinting brush
Spike comb
Sectioning clips
Large pins

Application

Add the hydrogen peroxide to the bleach, using a measure, and mix into a paste.

1. Pin the hair into clean sections working from the front to the nape. This must be accurate as it is the foundation of the entire process.

40

2. Starting at the nape, finely weave the hair with a spike comb taking approximately ten highlights every time.

3. It is important to weave just behind the hairline to avoid instant regrowth.

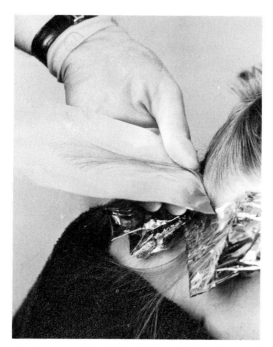

4. Place a strip of aluminium foil underneath the isolated strands, keeping it secure with the finger of your left hand (or right if you are left handed).

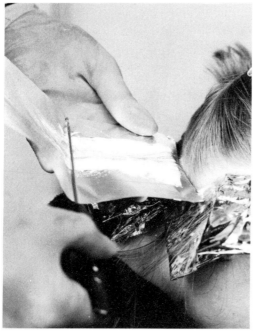

5. Brush on the bleach, carefully covering all the strands, and use the spike comb to crease the foil before folding it over.

42

6. Then fold both sides in the same way . . .

7. . . . and, finally, fold the end over again making a neat parcel.

8. Fold another piece of foil into a long strip . . .

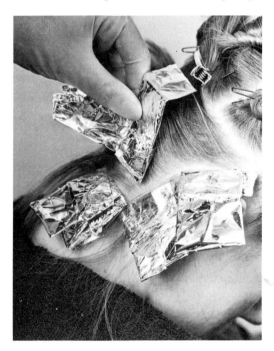

9. . . . and wrap around the base of the parcel to help keep it in position.

10. Continue using this method, working from the nape upwards.

11. Eventually there should be approximately 100 parcels although the number will depend on the thickness of the desired highlighting effect.

It takes approximately 45 minutes to weave an entire head and the equivalent time for developing, so start removing the first highlights as soon as the last ones are completed. Rinse throughly. I never advise using heat to speed up this process because the bleach would then expand rapidly, 'exploding' through the aluminium foil and creating a bleached effect on the rest of the hair.

Another word on weaving. Imagine a bricklayer building a wall; he avoids placing one brick directly above another so there are no vertical lines in the mortar binding the bricks. This is an excellent parallel to highlighting—the colourist must avoid creating vertical stripes in the hair.

Retouching

After three months the client will require a colour retouch on the front hairline, the natural parting and the crown. This will last a further three months before highlighting should be repeated on the roots of the entire head. At this stage, it is important only to apply the colour to the regrowth. The ends of the hair must be avoided otherwise an overall bleached effect will result.

Aim for a perfect combination of tone. Never, for example, create white streaks in black hair. Apply chestnut and dark red tones on brown shades, titian and marmalade tones on red shades and blonde tones on mousy shades.

It is unnecessary to use an oxidizing toner on very light highlights because they have already been bleached to the required shade. When peroxide toners are used on light highlights they have a slight lightening effect on the hair's natural colour and regrowth will become obvious a month later. The ideal base colour for highlights is mousy blonde.

Tinted Lights

Tinted lights are successful on all brown and mousy shades. Instead of bleaching the highlights, apply a tint by using the weaving method. The result is a natural-looking movement of colour rather than a highlighted effect. Clients with tinted lights tell me that friends suddenly remark, 'You're so lucky to have that hair colour *naturally!*'

Lowlights

An extremely mild bleach can be used to lift the lights slightly lighter than tinted lights but not quite as light as highlights. This method is suitable for very light brown hair (bleach highlights to a golden colour and apply a colour conditioner over the top to achieve a russet colour) or for a cream effect in blonde hair.

The colourist can utilize highlighting to emphasize the line of a cut. Example: The D.A. style (hair is swept back at the sides to the centre nape) can be promoted with a three-dimensional highlighting effect. Apply tinted lights to the crown section to give an appearance of depth of colour; the sides and nape are highlighted. The finished look gives a three-dimensional effect because the light sides are swept back over the darker crown section.

I have developed a variety of highlighting effects to accentuate individual styles and lengths of hair: halo, skull cap, Alice band of flashes, rim, strip, tortoise shell, shading and painted lights.

Halo

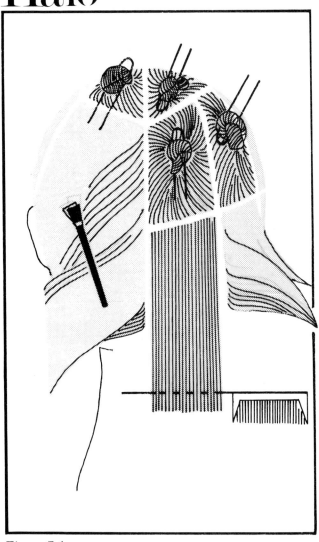

Figure 7.1

Halo Highlights

This highlighting effect is most successful on layered hair which is 4 to 6 inches in length. Note: Take care over the sectioning as this determines the finished result. Firstly, take a clean section at the crown and grip the hair up as this section will not be highlighted. Trace a parting from the centre back and another across the top of the head—from ear to ear. As shown in figure 7.1, this creates four basic sections for highlighting; the fifth is at the front. According to the size of the client's head, it may be necessary to divide the hair into slightly larger sections but I would generally recommend taking 2 inch wide sections.

Begin highlighting the ends of the hair on the right side of the back. Taking fine sections, weave approximately 12 highlights from the roots of the hair. Place aluminium foil underneath the highlights—pulling the foil down to the last 2 inches of the hair. Apply the bleach or tint and fold the foil into parcels. Continue in this way, working towards the crown and making sure that one highlight is not overlapping another. Repeat on the left side of the back, then the left side of the head, the right side of the head and, finally, the front section.

After removing the highlights from the foil, thoroughly rinse the hair, section-by-section, to avoid a bleached effect on the natural hair. Shampoo and condition the entire head as normal. The finished result will be a subtle halo effect—the natural top section eliminates any possibility of a solid rim around the ends of the hair.

Skullcap Highlights

Short, layered styles are ideal for skullcap highlighting. Trace a skullcap shaped section on the top on the head and divide this into four triangular sections (see figure 7.2).

Start weaving the highlights from the right side at the back. Work upwards towards the top of the triangle, leaving a smaller triangle at the top of the initial section. Weave the left side at the back in the same way, again leaving a smaller triangle at the top of the section. Comb the two smaller triangles together and weave the hair very finely, taking sections across the head. Leave a fine section of hair at the centre which will be combed over the highlights. (The reason for this is to avoid highlighting on a parting.) Repeat on the left front section and, finally, the right front section.

Tip Highlights

I recommend using tip highlighting on curly styles. Section the hair in the same way as the basic highlighting technique. Since the highlights are larger than for the previous two methods, larger sections must be taken in between weaving the highlights to avoid an all-over colour tone. Note: Do not take the bleach or toner too close to the roots—only the last ½ to 2 inches of each section is highlighted.

Skull Cap

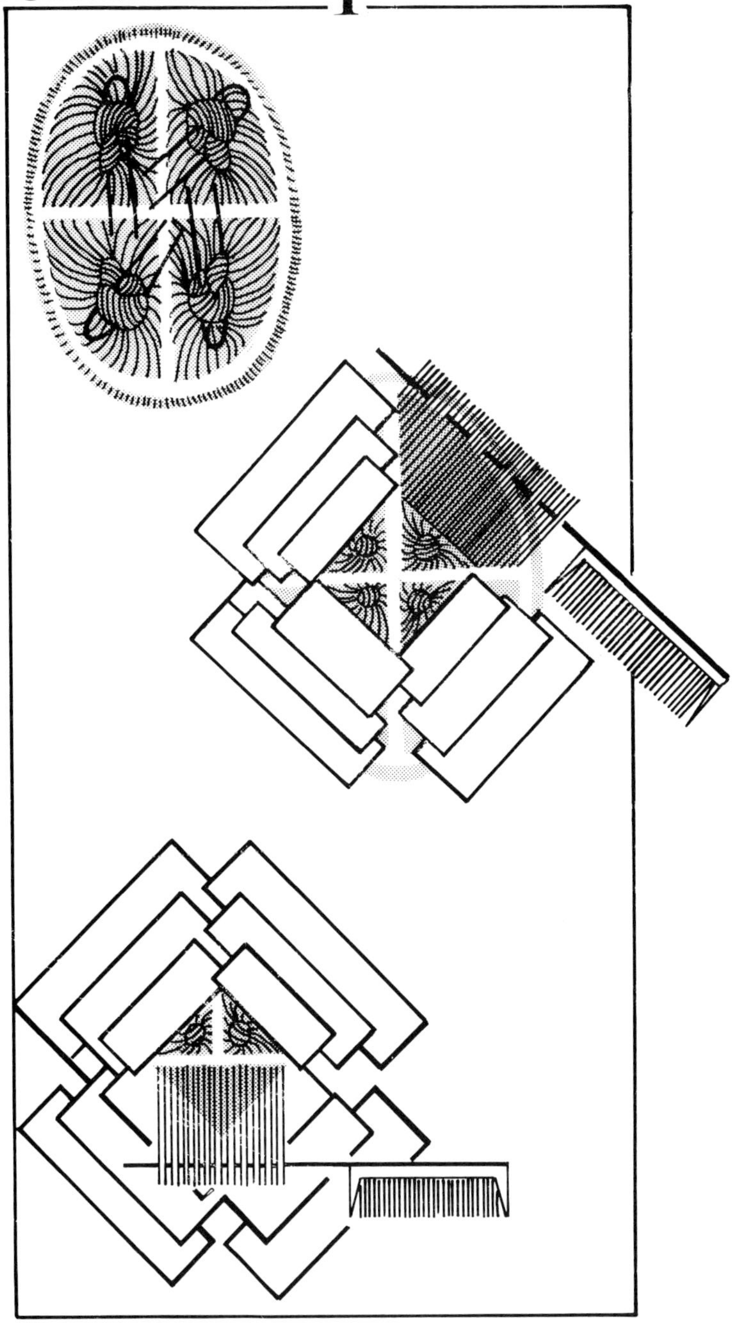

Figure 7.2

Alice Band

Figure 7.3

Alice Band of Flashes

The Alice band of flashes can be achieved on any type of hair, long or short, curly or straight. One factor that determines the success of this effect is,the way in which the hair is worn afterwards. I prefer to use a style with a side parting where the hair softly flicks back off the face. It is a good idea to call the stylist over, prior to highlighting, to position the parting and perhaps start blow styling so that you know exactly how the hair will fall.

Divide the hair to create a ½ inch strip across the front of the head. The Alice band will be the ½ inch strip immediately behind the first section (see figure 7.3). Ensure all the hair in the front section and the hair behind the Alice band is completely out of the way.

Start highlighting on a ½ inch square section just above the ear. Continue taking ½ inch sections, working upwards to within ½ inch of the parting. Repeat on the other side of the head, again leaving the last section natural to disguise any obvious lines and to avoid an instant regrowth.

The range of colour choice for the band of flashes is unlimited—from subtle, natural effects to the bright crazy colours. The band can either be highlighted in one colour or in several different ones, but when using a combination of colours, always remember to keep the hair in the rest of the band completely away from the section being coloured.

Rim Highlights

This highlighting effect is most successful on mid length hair with a full fringe, combed forwards from the crown; the rest of the hair is cut to one length, flicking slightly outwards at the ends. Method: Trace a parting across the head—from ear to ear—and comb the fringe section forwards. This section will be left natural so grip the hair up to keep it completely away from the bleach or tint. Take a semi-circular section at the crown, which will be left natural, and then trace a centre parting down the back, dividing the hair into two basic sections for highlighting (see figure 7.4).

Start by taking sections as a complete strip—*not* weaving the hair—around the rim of the right side of the back. Place the aluminium foil underneath these sections and pull the foil down to the ends of the hair. Apply the bleach or tint to the last 1½ inches of the hair and fold the foil into neat parcels. Work upwards, taking ¼ inch sections (the strip lights will be the top ⅛ inch of these sections) until within ½ inch of the parting. Note: Continue to pull the foil down towards the ends of the hair before applying the bleach or tint.

Now *weave* highlights into the remaining ½ inch section—this gradually breaks down the heaviness of the rim. Repeat on the left side of the back. This effect can be easily adapted for hair which is all one length, again slightly flicking outwards at the ends, but without a fringe. Divide the head into four sections and repeat the method used for the back sections on the two front sections. As with the back sections, remember to leave out an overlapping section of approximately ½ inch on the top layers which will be left natural.

The finished effect is a vibrant rim shining through the hair rather than a solid rim which could look like an old tint or bleach growing out!

Rim

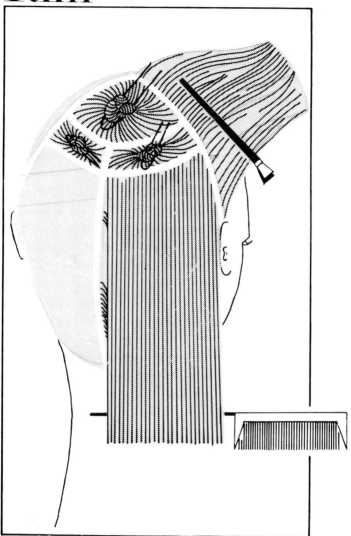

Figure 7.4

Strip Highlights

This type of highlighting is ideal for creating a beautiful blonde effect in mousy blonde hair or any shade lighter. It is particularly suitable for the client who does not want to return to the salon every three to four weeks for maintenance. (Figure 7.5.)

Sectioning is exactly the same as for the basic highlighting technique. But instead of weaving, take out ¼ inch sections of hair and apply the bleach to the top ⅛ inch of each section and wrap in

Strip

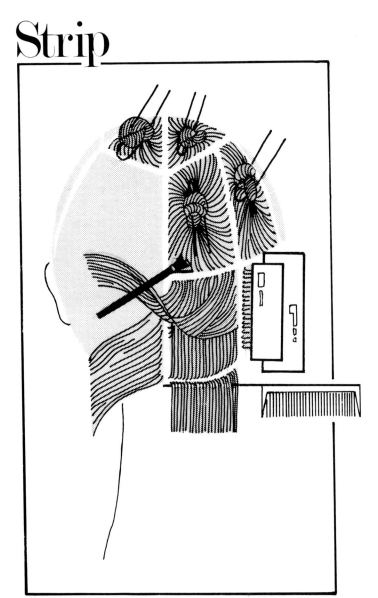

Figure 7.5

aliminium foil as normal. The weaving method is used, however, for the last few sections before the parting in order to avoid an instant regrowth.

Tortoise Shell Highlights

Tortoise shell highlighting is suitable for all brown shades of hair. Choose three contrasting colours (e.g. honey blonde, hazel and titian) and mix separately. Section the head in the same way as the basic highlighting technique but alternate the three colours in each section to create an even distribution of colour.

Shading Lights

This is another method of using two or three different colours for lights in the hair and is particularly effective on a light brown base. Section the hair as in the basic highlighting technique and take ½ inch sections, applying the tint to the top ⅛ inch of each section as with strip highlighting. Apply the three colours in alternate strips to create a shading effect.

Painted Lights

Painted lights can be a great asset for a client who has just had a tint applied to her hair. After rinsing off the tint, comb the hair back off the face and paint fine streaks through the front section with a mild solution of bleach. Rinse the streaks off after 10 to 15 minutes according to the lightness required. This technique helps to create extra movement and subtlety in tinted hair.

Photograph by Barry Lategan.
Hair by Leonard.
Colour by Daniel.

By permission of VOGUE, copyright ©1970 by The Conde Nast Publications Inc.
Photograph by Clive Arrowsmith.
Hair by Leonard.
Colour by Daniel.

By permission of Wella (Great Britain) Limited.
Photograph by David Bailey.
Hair by Leonard.
Colour by Daniel.

By permission of VOGUE Italia.
Photograph by Barry Lategan.
Hair by Leonard.
Colour by Daniel.

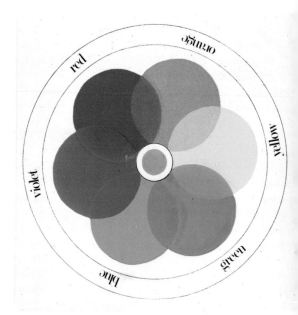

8. Vegetable Colours

Henna. As old as time itself, yet as new as tomorrow.

HENNA is one of the oldest forms of hair colouring, dating back thousands of years before Christ. Although it has not been popular in the Western world during the last hundred years, it is now beginning to play an important role, as an extra service, in the hair colouring business because people are generally becoming more health conscious and demanding natural products on their hair.

Vegetable henna originates from the *Lawsonia* plant which grows throughout Africa and Asia, varying in strength from country to country. Moroccan henna has more orange pigment and is least valuable in terms of conditioning agents. The further one travels towards Iran, the redder the pigment of the henna becomes and the better it acts as a conditioner, thus making the Persian variety the most sought after in the world.

Henna is most commonly used to create a beautiful sheen on the naturally dark hair of Eastern women. Another popular use in some parts of the world is to paint henna on the soles of the feet and the palms of the hands in order to prevent perspiration. It is also used for painting figures over the bodies of young brides—a similar idea to tattooing. These girls then colour their finger and toe nails with henna as part of the matrimonial ceremony. Another established use of henna is as an ancient medical remedy.

Henna is prepared, after being cropped in November, by drying the leaves in the sun, removing the veins and then crushing the remainder into powder.

Application

The traditional method of mixing henna is to add hot water and stir into a creamy paste. I have devised my own favourite formula: add hot, black coffee to the powder and mix into a smooth paste, then add the juice of a fresh lemon and the yolk of an egg. The coffee brings out the depth and richness of the hair colour, the acid in the lemon accelerates the red, and the egg yolk keeps the mixture moist and easy to manoeuvre through the hair. Henna can also be mixed with 10 vol. (3%) peroxide to create a light, fire-crystallising colour.

Apply henna in the same way as a whole head tint, treating the middle lengths and ends first, and when the colour is half-developed, apply to the roots. Leave on the hair for a period of up to an hour, depending on the base colour and the depth of the colour required. The darker the base colour, the more chestnut the result. The lighter the natural colour, the more titian the stain.

Although extremely successful on brunettes and black hair, the previous formulation will not achieve the same effect on mousy hair.

55

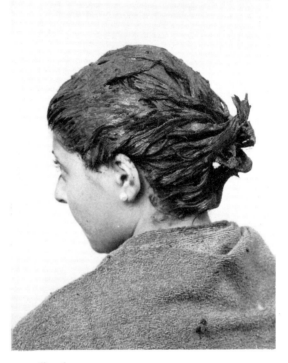

A whole head henna application

It usually results in a nondescript, orange/red tone. After numerous experiments, I have discovered that the best way to create a titian effect on mousy shades is to mix hot red wine with henna.

Other ideas for mixing ingredients include vinegar and black tea. In order to give a more coppery effect try dropping a couple of copper coins into a henna mixture. This probably sounds absurd but you will be amazed at the result! Within 30 minutes the coins will resemble a combination of new copper and silver coins which gives you some idea of the amount of copper which henna will extract from an ordinary coin.

The adventurous colourist who wants to achieve vibrant colours with henna should try applying the henna as normal, covering the head with a plastic cap and then placing the client under a dryer for up to one hour.

Retouching

When the client returns to have her roots retouched, the henna should be applied for approximately 30 minutes to the roots and then combed through for another 15 to 30 minutes. Henna gives a permanent stain and creates a build up of colour so re-application in this way will prevent the hair from turning too red on the ends.

56

When Not to Use Henna

Never use henna over a tint as it is inclined to lift out the artificial colour and produce an uneven result. I would also not recommend using henna on grey hair as it will become 'carroty' and unnatural.

Note: Avoid compound hennas. These are available in all colours from black to blonde but they contain metallic substances which may cause a chemical reaction if a tint or permanent wave is applied afterwards.

Compound hennas are unstable and take anything up to 24 hours to develop. I can illustrate this best by describing a client I knew as a student colourist myself. She came into the salon every four weeks with a one-inch regrowth of white hair. The rest of her hair was dyed black with a compound henna. A hot, muddy paste was applied to the hair and the head would then be covered with newspaper and left for a period of up to one hour. After rinsing off the colour, the entire regrowth had remained pure white, and neutralising tablets were applied in a liquid form and left on the hair for 10 minutes.

By the time her hair had been set and she was ready to leave the salon, the white hair had a yellowish tinge. She would then return to the salon after 24 hours to have her hair combed out, by which time the hair had been oxidised to a dark brown/black base—the desired colour *finally* achieved by the compound henna! (Hair which has been treated in this way should never be subsequently permed or tinted.)

In the case of a Far Eastern client, remember that henna is left on the head for anything up to 48 hours in her home country (during which time it is continually basted with oil to prevent it from drying out). These women have very dark hair and it is advisable to mix henna with 10 vol. (3%) peroxide to achieve the same results within an hour.

Again, I cannot stress enough, **never use pure henna in any other colour than red.** (The natural red pigment comes from the leaves so the dye itself looks green although it will colour the hair red.) In my opinion, there is only one safe black henna to use on the hair—a combination of indigo and natural red henna. Indigo is blue and when mixed with henna will counteract the red, producing a dark brown shade. This is known as black Persian henna and does not contain any metallic substances.

If in doubt of the type of product being used, take a peroxide and ammonia test on the henna mixture. If it effervesces, the henna contains metallic substances but if not, it is safe to apply to the hair.

Numerous other vegetable products can be used by the colourist to achieve a particular effect—all leaving the hair in excellent condition afterwards. But, remember that these dyes are time-consuming—usually taking several applications to achieve a similar result as that obtained by using one application of today's oxidation dyes. Here are just some of the dyes which I have experimented with and successfully used in the salon:

57

Chamomile

This herb has a slight lightening effect on the hair. The chamomile infusion is a similar method to making tea; one pint of boiling water and the chamomile are left to brew for 10 to 15 minutes, according to the strength required. When cold, strain off the liquid and apply to the hair as a final rinse.

Although chamomile has a lightening effect on the hair, it will only achieve this after several applications, whereas peroxide will lift the hair almost instantly. However, I find it a great asset to give a very soft lightening effect to naturally blonde hair twice a year by regular use, for instance, throughout the months of October and March.

Rhubarb Root

Rhubarb root is one of the best hair lighteners that I have ever used. It is far stronger than chamomile—in fact it is probably the strongest of all lightening herbal colours. To use, add boiling water and boil for anything up to an hour, leave until cold and use as a final rinse. Best results are achieved by leaving the hair in the sun after application. This will give golden highlights to the hair—even after the first application. This particular method works on all types of natural hair bases—producing the following results:

Black hair	—	Chestnut overtones
Light Brown hair	—	Light Chestnut tones
Mousy hair	—	Golden overtones
Light Ash Blonde hair	—	Light Golden tones

To accelerate the development time, add the juice of a lemon to the liquid before it is applied to the hair.

Saffron

Whenever I mention saffron most people immediately think of saffron rice which is, of course, dyed with saffron. Although it is one of the most expensive herbs in the world, the vibrant tones that can be achieved with saffron are exceptional, usually resulting in a luminous canary-yellow colour.

In order to obtain as much dye stuff as possible, boil the saffron root with water for 15 to 30 minutes. This concentrated solution can then be diluted according to the depth of colour required. Apply by using the same method as a temporary water rinse.

Marigold

Another method of achieving very soft yellow tones on white hair or highly bleached hair is by using marigolds. This dye is prepared by the infusion method and applied as a final rinse.

Important: When using any of these herbal dyes you must have a base light enough to achieve the effect required. Example: If applying saffron to a dark brown base the result will be a dark brown colour—if you want to achieve a vivid yellow, saffron must be used on a very light base. If the hair is dark and you want to achieve, say, a flash in the side of the hair, the flash must initially be bleached almost white or to a pale lemon before applying the saffron dip (as I call it) to achieve the vibrant yellow tone.

Sage

This useful salon herb is mixed and applied in the same way as chamomile, but has a dulling effect, thereby slightly darkening greying hair. If a greater darkening effect is required, upgrade the amount of herbs to the same quantity of boiling water.

Cascarilla

In ancient times, one of the major colourants for grey hair was made up from boiling the barks of trees for one to two hours. (Today, their main use is for tanning hide.) Numerous types of trees can be used to achieve different depths of tone, but the one that I have found particularly successful is cascarilla which yields a strong black dye. Prepare by the infusion method and apply as a final rinse.

Walnuts

Another method of dying grey hair is to make a paste by burning walnuts (other nuts can also be used), grinding them into a fine powder and mixing them with a little water. This gives a temporary dulling effect to slightly greying hair which can be washed out the following day, if required. A more permanent colour can be achieved by boiling the nuts for longer than two hours. The more often the rinse is applied, the darker it will colour the hair.

If you are interested in experimenting in the field of herbal colours, it is a good idea to contact a local herbalist for guidance. With the combination of ancient herbs and modern day chemistry, the colourist is able to achieve better results than ever before. It is ironical that although these herbs are thousands of years old, we are only in the experimental stage of exploiting them in the 20th century. This is only the beginning . . . an entire new field is just waiting to be opened up by the progressive colourist!

9. Aftercare

THE major hairdressing 'C's'—Cut and Colour—are teamed with another of equal importance: Condition. Unfortunately, this is often relegated to a minor role in some salons. Always study the client's hair at the beginning of each appointment because the condition can vary from one week to another. The hair must be in perfect condition before colouring—this extra attention will contribute enormously to the final result.

Reasons for Poor Condition

1. Strong detergent shampoo, and the purifiers in our tap water.
2. Incorrect use of heated rollers, dryers, brushes and combs.
3. Tinting and perming (although colouring beautifies the hair, it also removes some of the natural oils).
4. Deposits of chemical waste from today's polluted atmosphere.

Whilst the body has the digestive system to retain the good and reject the bad, the hair has no such natural aid, and it is therefore up to you—the professional—to maintain the hair's lustre. The key factor in keeping hair in good condition is cleanliness and this will vary from one client to another. Whilst a weekly shampoo is sufficient for some, others may require more washes. Whatever the frequency of shampooing, always choose a suitable shampoo for the particular hair type, taking the condition of the scalp into consideration. Use your professional integrity and not just the nearest bottle to hand!

Diet also plays a major part in determining the hair's condition. In cases where the hair is greasy, recommend that the client avoids all greasy and fried foods, too many spices and strong seasonings which can over-activate the sebaceous glands. The majority of people with a greasy hair problem, wash their hair practically every day in an effort to remove the grease. Advise these clients to shampoo their hair in the normal way but without massaging their head as this only serves to activate the sebaceous glands. Instead, lather the shampoo by rubbing the palm of the hand over the head. I would also suggest using an astringent lotion on the roots of the hair every day. This will help to dry up the grease and allow the client to leave her hair for longer periods before washing.

If the client is generally run-down the hair will follow suit. (Certain forms of medication will affect the hair's condition so make a tactful enquiry about any recent illness or treatment prescribed.) Personally, I feel that this can often be attributed to today's fast pace of living, especially with the popular awareness of weight-watching. All too often, people on diets neglect the body's essential vitamins. In these cases, I recommend a course of Vitamin B with added

61

Vitamin C. The specific vitamins are as follows: Nicotinamide, Thiamine Hydrochloride, Pyridoxine Hydrochloride, Riboflavin (all Vitamin B) and Ascorbic Acid (Vitamin C). This is important to the hairdresser because the body must have the correct nourishment in order to promote healthy hair. Example: When we suffer with influenza, the hair is immediately affected and it takes a couple of weeks before it regains its original condition. Yeast is also excellent for contributing to healthy hair but is unfortunately fattening and therefore unacceptable to clients who are dieting.

Recent investment and research into hair care has meant that manufacturers' products have become increasingly sophisticated. Today's hairdresser can buy the ultimate in hair care—not simply one product for greasy hair, another for dry hair, etc.—there are now ranges offering anything up to 40 different lotions or creams enabling you to prescribe the exact product for each individual client.

Whether you use the manufacturers' products, or you devise your own, as I do, there is no justification for dry, lifeless hair after tinting. Remember: All the time and effort involved in colouring the hair is wasted if the hair lapses into poor condition afterwards. Whatever is taken out of the hair during the colouring process, must be replaced. Make sure every client has a conditioner or aftercare treatment of some kind. Aftercare is essential, even for hair that was originally in good condition, in order to maintain the same healthy state.

As I have just mentioned, I devise my own treatments. These are as follows:

1. Organic Protein

I always recommend an organic protein treatment after a bleach or an oxidation dye as it will have destroyed a proportion of the hair's cuticle. This treatment comprises 100% hydrolised organic protein which has been broken down to molecular size to enable penetration of the hair shaft and help rebuild the outer cuticle. In chapter 1, I explained that the hair consists of 22 amino acids which form protein, and, when oxidised, become keratin. These also form the hard, cement-like outer cuticle. When a client's hair is dull it is probably because the cuticle is rough and damaged instead of lying flat. This means the light cannot reflect off the rough edges, thus preventing a normal sheen. Apply 1 oz. of the organic protein after shampooing and leave for ten minutes before rinsing thoroughly. Note the difference between a treatment and a conditioner. The protein treatment will actually help to rebuild the hair after processing but if the hair is naturally dry it will remain coarse after the protein is washed off. The cream conditioner can then be used to moisten the hair and make it easier to comb.

2. pH Balancer

If a pH balancer is used after applying bleach or an oxidation colour, which are alkaline based (see chapter 2), it will return the hair to its normal pH balance. This treatment will help to shrink the 'swollen' processed hair back to its normal size and prevent breakage or splitting between visits to the salon.

3. Cream Treatment

The cream treatment consists of a protein cream with avocado oil or Vitamin E wheatgerm oil and is particularly effective on dry scalps or dry hair. The basis of my cream treatment is an ordinary emulsifying wax—it is the added protein that helps brittle hair to regain its original elasticity after a bleach or an oxidation dye. Both avocado oil and Vitamin E are effective in nourishing dry skin.

4. Herbal Treatment

The herbal treatment is a perfect cleanser giving beautiful sheen and body to all types of hair. It comprises dried hibiscus flowers, myrtle, olive leaves and lotus blossom. Hibiscus is an excellent conditioning agent. As an experiment, crush some dried hibiscus flowers with a drop of water in the palms of your hands. Once the mixture has turned to pulp, rinse your hands under water and, however dry your hands were originally, they will now feel soft, silky and lustrous. Myrtle, olive leaves and lotus blossom are all effective cleansers and skin healers without stripping the natural oils from the hair. These ingredients are mixed with hot water and an egg yolk. Apply to the hair and leave for 15 to 20 minutes before rinsing thoroughly and shampooing in the normal way. If using this treatment on fine, greasy hair, do not add the egg yolk.

Note: Home maintenance obviously plays an important role in aftercare. Make sure your client is using the correct products—treatment, shampoo and conditioner—at home in between colour applications.

10. Colouring for Magazines, Television and Films

ALL fashion colouring effects must be stronger than normal. The camera usually tones colours down so they have to be fairly vibrant in order to look subtle. Experiment with different materials like acid dyes, poster colours, Indian inks and silk dyes.

If you are working on a model, see her a couple of days before the photographic session or show. The hair will probably have to be cut, then coloured, cut again, coloured again—sometimes for three consecutive days before the desired result is achieved. Always look out for new models—whether they are professionals or simply pretty clients.

Try to keep ahead of fashion through a constant awareness of the forthcoming season's colours. It is important to have a good photographer, make-up artist and clothes or all your time and effort will have been in vain! Work as a team, always being receptive to other people's advice and ideas.

Crazy Colour

My first publicity with crazy colour was in 1966 with a double page spread in *Queen* magazine (as it was then called). I had coloured a wig with six or seven vivid shades of green—from emerald to lime green. At that time, fashion designer Zandra Rhodes had a growing popularity in the magazines—and her fantasy patterns and colours inspired the use of crazy colour in the hair.

Obviously, I did not intend this to become a high street fashion but hoped that it would make women more hair colour *conscious* than ever before. It did; people started asking, 'If that's what they can do with hair colour today, what can they do to improve my hair?'

Before applying crazy colour, bleach the hair and shampoo in the normal way. Apply the colour according to the desired result; dilute for a temporary colour or use a more concentrated solution for a longer-lasting result. Example: For someone as extrovert as Zandra Rhodes (who is now a client of mine) I have to apply the colour so that it will last until her next visit to the salon in two months time. These colours can sometimes be so strong that her hair has to be shampooed about eight times in order to remove the excess colour.

In addition to magazines, colour opens up enormous scope for television and film work. Unfortunately, one of the problems with bright colours is that they are often exposed to extremely strong lights which have a slight bleaching effect on the artificial pigmentation. A great deal of maintenance is therefore required to keep the colour constant, and conditioning treatments are essential.

I am often employed as a hair colour consultant for television which has meant working for such stars as Lulu, Cilla Black, Petula

Clark, Kiki Dee, Olivia Newton John and Mama Cass. There are some important points to note when colouring for television, e.g. a redhead will appear much brighter on the screen than in real life.

Again it is amazing how many problems can be encountered in colouring for films. During the period when Twiggy was working on *The Boyfriend,* the camera picked up a tiny regrowth on her highlights—so I was required on the film set in Portsmouth every five to seven days to tint her parting and hairline.

In *Murder on the Orient Express,* Albert Finney's mousy blonde hair had to be coloured black and sleeked down for a detective look. But, he was simultaneously appearing in a London theatre which meant washing the colour off daily. In order to achieve the effect, I mixed a black pomade and the only way the colour could be removed was by using Swarfega (a special chemical used by motor mechanics for removing grease).

Nine months' research was necessary to create the wigs for *Barry Lyndon.* It is important that the hair colourist researches into the ways the colours were actually achieved in history. In this film, Marisa Berenson's part necessitated dark hair contrasting with white make-up. Unfortunately, her hair had been coloured with henna for a previous film, and the only way to remove the red pigment was with concentrated ash tones.

I spent a great deal of time experimenting with futuristic crazy colours for *2001* and *A Clockwork Orange.* In the case of *A Clockwork Orange,* over 100 wigs and hairpieces were dyed for the cast in addition to travelling to the film studios to apply painted lights to some of the actors' and actresses' hair.

Famous personalities (particularly pop stars) are usually the most difficult people work with. This is where the psychological side of the hairdressing business plays an important part; it is essential to be able to handle everybody—whatever walk of life they may come from. Although, I have to admit that I was slightly taken off guard when Lauren Bacall came to Britain to star in *Applause.* Her first words to me were, 'Get me a large vodka on the rocks NOW!'

On another occasion, I was asked by a film company in Spain to give a blue sheen to a black horse. I mixed an enormous quantity of a concentrated navy blue with water in a horse bath . . . it worked!

Daniel Galvin

DANIEL GALVIN, born in 1944, left school at the age of 15 to work as a junior in a hairdressing salon in London's West End. At that time, the job involved sweeping up, washing the basins and scrubbing the pavement outside the salon. But Daniel was not deterred by this lack of glamour as he already had an insight into the hairdressing world; his grandfather, father, brother and sister were all in the hairdressing trade.

His second job was in a suburban salon where he was promoted to shampooing and, eventually, to setting hair. But it was with hair *colouring* aspirations that Daniel then wrote to the top ten London salons of that time. Olofson of Knightsbridge was the only one to reply and, aged 18, he was given the job. It was not until one of the tinters at Olofson was taken ill for three months, that Daniel began tinting; it was then that his unusual flair for hair colouring was first discovered.

After having specialized in tinting for nine months, news of Daniel's talent reached Vidal Sasoon and Leonard—then Britain's two young rival leaders—and both approached him with offers to join them. It was a difficult decision but eventually he chose Leonard who had plans for launching the largest salon in London with the largest tinting department in Europe. Within a fortnight of having worked for Leonard, Daniel was promoted to head of the tinting department. Four years later he became a director of the company and is now a partner with Leonard. During this period he has built up an 18-strong team of colourists and has trained many of the tinters in London's top salons.

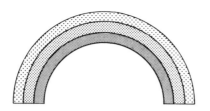

Hair Colour Consultants Limited

Founded and Personally Directed by **DANIEL GALVIN**
makes available his services as Creative Colour Consultant.
For information on seminars, teach-ins and products
contact **DANIEL GALVIN**

Hair Colour Consultants, Ltd.,
43 Welbeck Street, London W.1 Tel: 01 486 6363/4/5/6 Telex 27689

A SIGN OF SUCCESS

Daniel Galvin, like thousands more throughout the country, is a Registered Hairdresser and holder of the Master Craftsman Diploma.

Although his talents and skills have brought him an international reputation and made his name synonymous with the finest hair colour work in a dozen or more countries, he is still very concerned about the hairdressing industry in Britain.

He supports the Hairdressing Council's efforts to make hairdressing a truly professional occupation in Britain — as it is in many other countries.

He wants every entrant to follow approved training courses.

He wants the public to have the protection of knowing that salon staff are qualified.

That's why he is a Registered Hairdresser.

That's why you should be a Registered Hairdresser.

For information about the Hairdressing Council and an application to register or for the Master Craftsman Diploma, write to

The Hairdressing Council,
17, Spring Street,
London W2 3RA

L'ORÉAL

speaks the language of hair beauty in 130 different countries.

ommunicating with millions of women who want to improve and emphasize
eir topmost beauty asset – their hair. To experience L'Oreal's wonderful ways
with hair is to discover a more colourful, prettier self.

ORÉAL's developments emanate from a search team of more than 700 scientists hroughout the world. It is especially in the Oreal cosmetic laboratories in Paris, which re among the most advanced in Europe, that o many new ways of making hair healthier, nore manageable and more beautiful are orn.

In Britain the name of L'Oreal is synonymous with Excellence, Preference and Unison S, which are the very best hair colourings, with conditioners, treatment shampoos and setting aids. Then there are sensational style supports like Demi-Wave and permanent waves, too. And, beautiful, beautiful Elnett Satin hairspray.

Say L'Oréal and speak the language of hair beauty . . . fluently.

world leaders i

air colouring

Throughout the world the name of Wella stands for high quality hair care products. Wella products are respected and trusted in no less than 130 countries. That is why the world's leading hair colourists insist upon... Wella.

WELLA
we know about hair

Indispensable....

"and the choice of professionals"

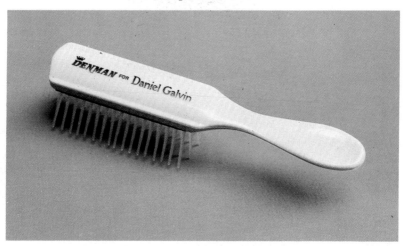

DENROY INTERNATIONAL LT
Denroy House
85 Brighton Road
Surbiton
Surrey KT6 5NX England
Telephone (01) 399 4151 (PBX)